Circles

Scamp is balancing on a circle.
Find all the circles.
Colour them red.

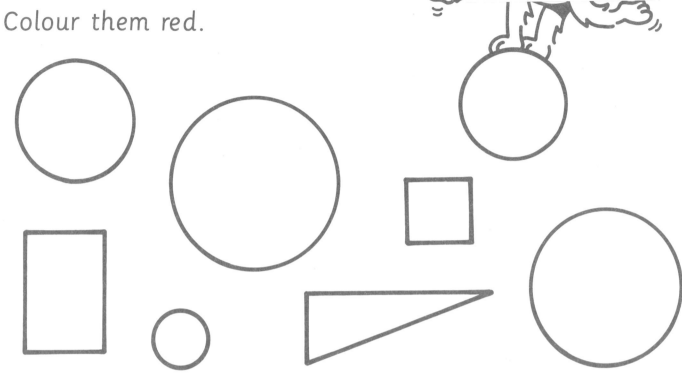

Look at Scamp and the clown.
Colour the circles red.

Shortest

Colour the shortest one.

Draw a shorter lead for Scamp.

Longest

Colour the longest one.

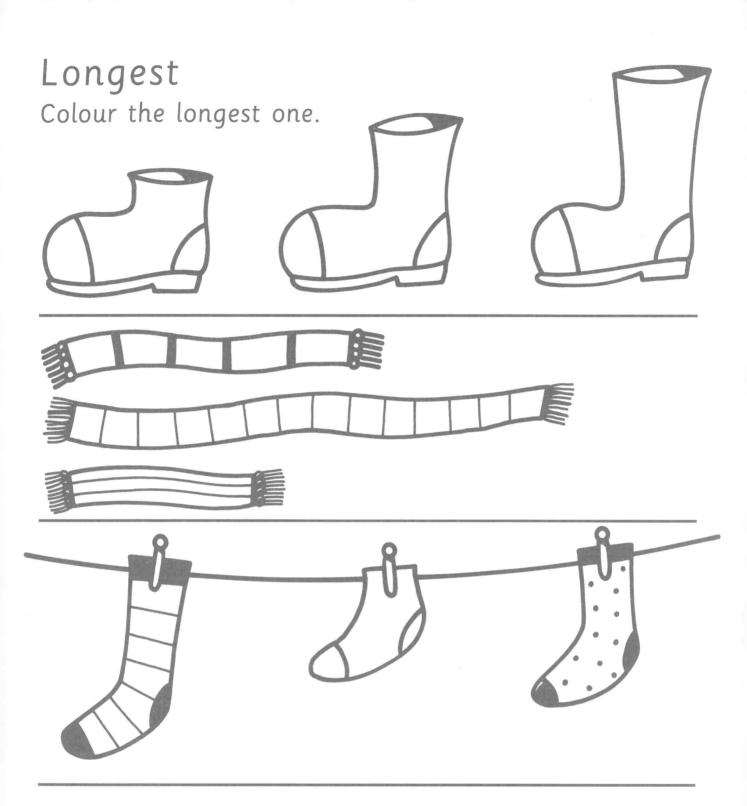

Draw a longer stick for Scamp to fetch.

Squares

Scamp is hiding behind a square.
Can you see more squares?
Colour them green.

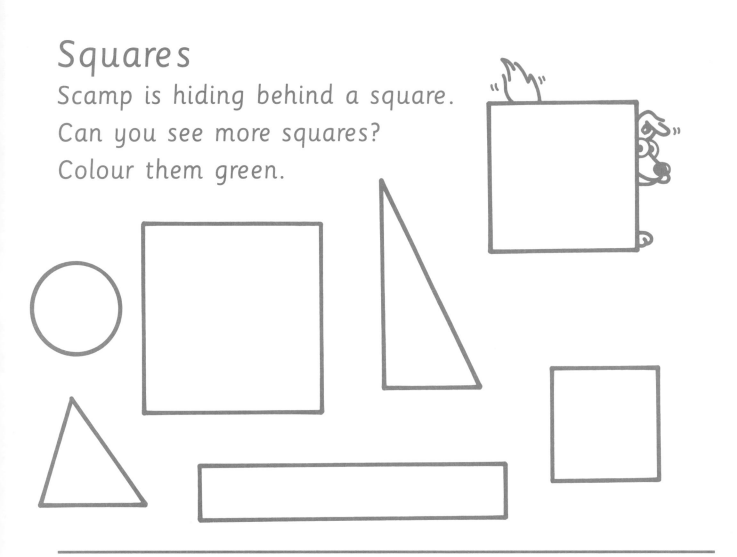

What is Scamp doing now? Colour the squares green.

Rectangles

Scamp is jumping over a rectangle. Find some more rectangles. Colour them blue.

Where is Scamp?
Colour the rectangles blue.

7

Smallest

Colour the smallest one.

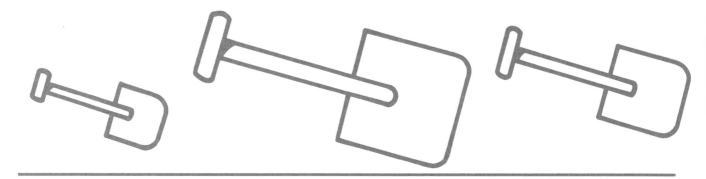

Draw a smaller ice-cream.

Biggest

Colour the biggest one.

Draw a bigger balloon for Scamp.

Matching 1 – 1

Give each flower a vase.

Give each tree an apple.

Give each leaf a ladybird.

Matching 1 – 1
Give each animal a home.

Matching Sets
Match the sets that have the same number in them.

Matching Sets

Match the sets that have the same number in them.

Sets with More

Look at each set.
Draw a new set with more in it.

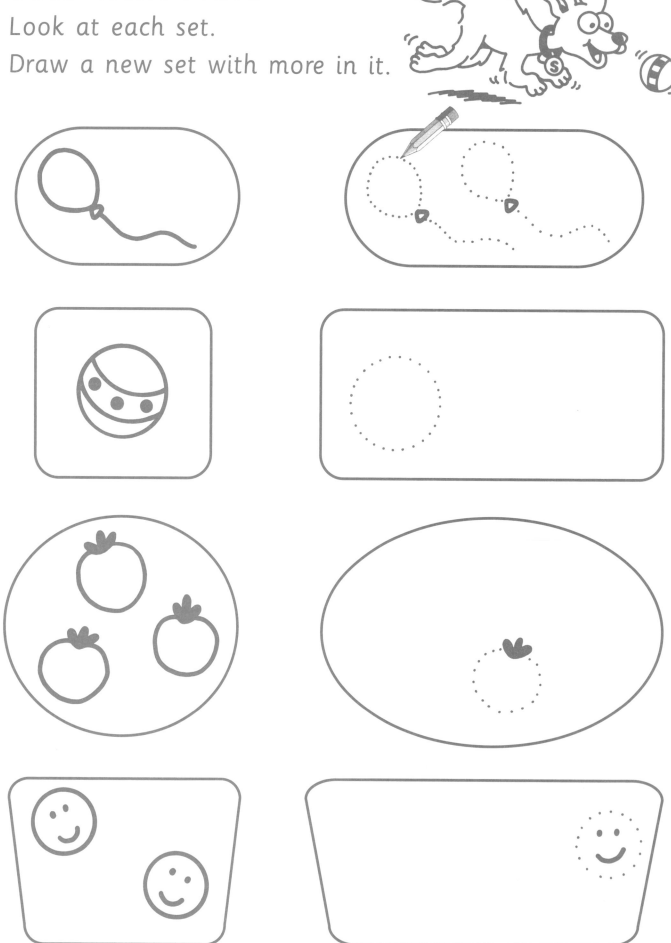

Sets with More

Look at each set.
Draw a new set with more in it.

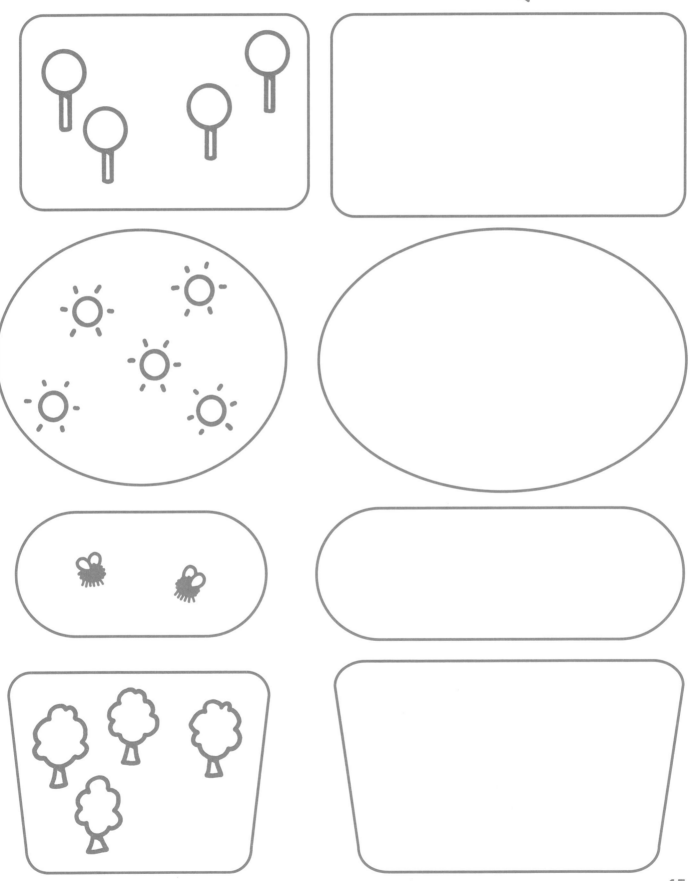

Sets with Less

Look at each set.

Draw a new set with less in it.

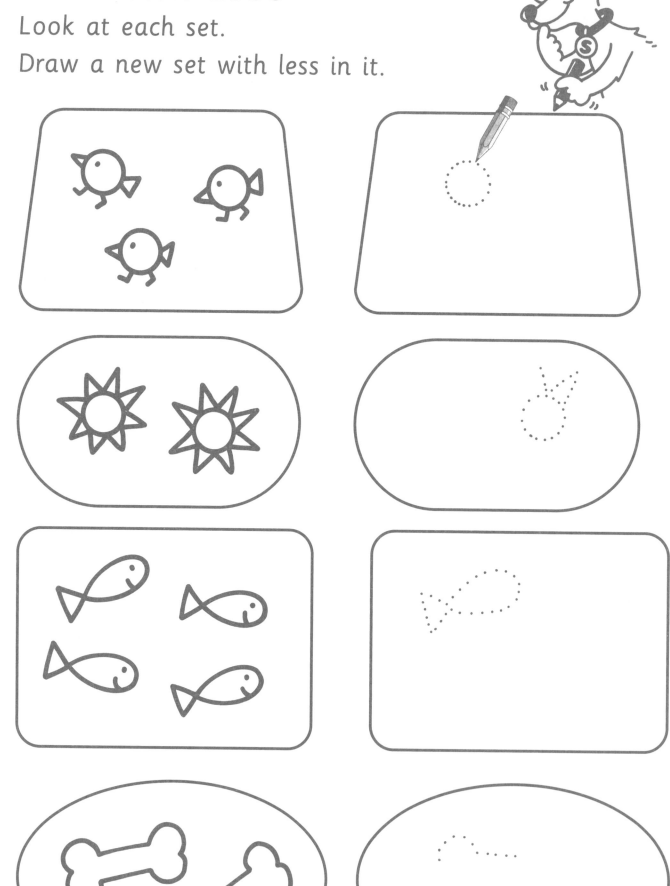

Sets with Less

Look at each set.

Draw a new set with less in it.

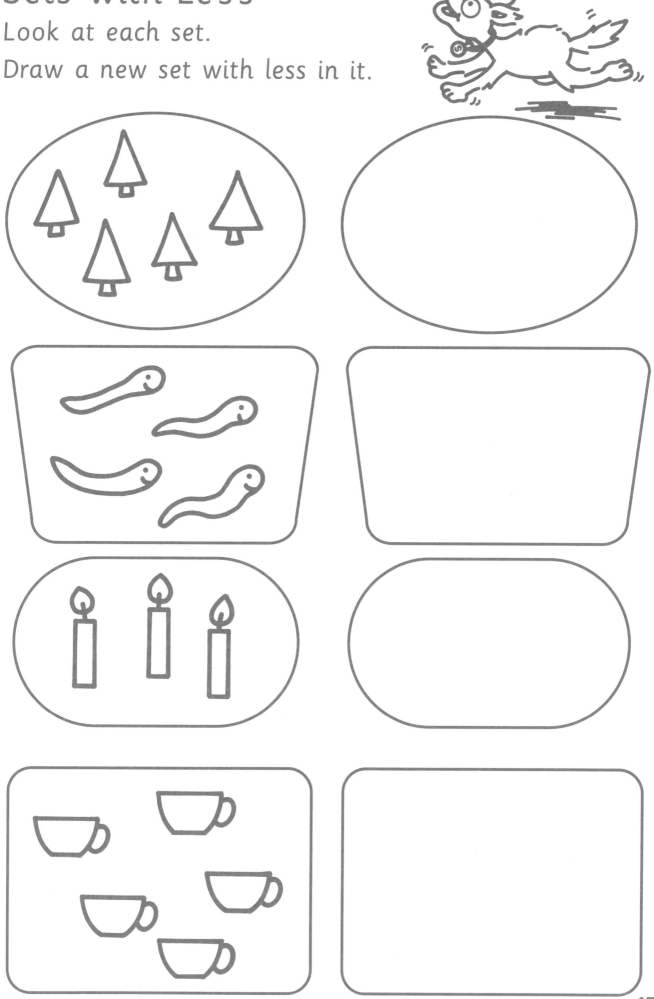

Matching Numbers

About 1. Count how many.
Write the number.

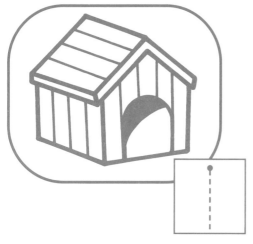  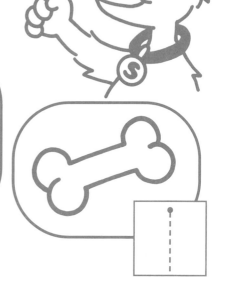

Draw 1 ball.   Draw 1 apple.   Draw 1 flower.

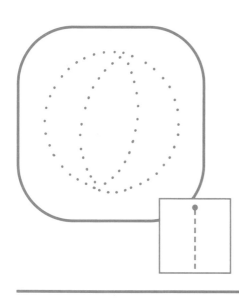 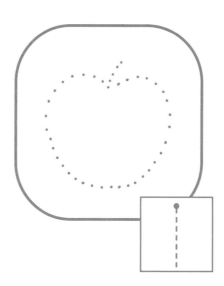 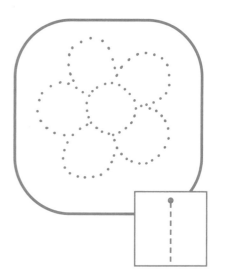

Join the sets of 1 to the number.

I

Matching Numbers

About 2. Count how many.
Write the number.

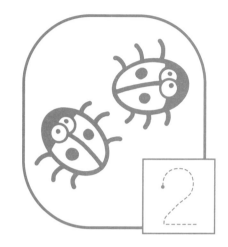

Draw 2 mugs.

Draw 2 glasses.

Draw 2 plates.

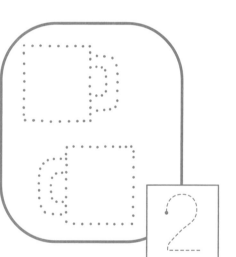
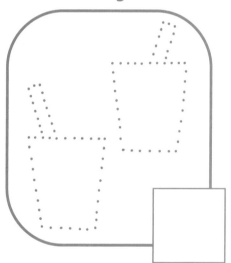
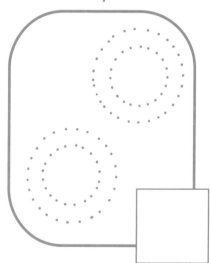

Join the sets of 2 to the number.

2

Matching Numbers

About I and 2.

Write the number.

I 2 I 2 I 2 I 2 I 2

Draw I baby in each pram.

Draw 2 leaves on each stick.

  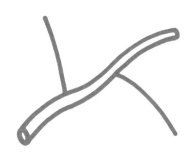

Colour the buns with I cherry.

Colour the vases with 2 flowers.

20

Matching Numbers

About 3. Count how many.
Write the number.

Draw 3 eggs.   Draw 3 chicks.   Draw 3 birds.

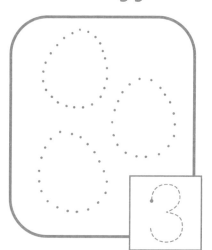 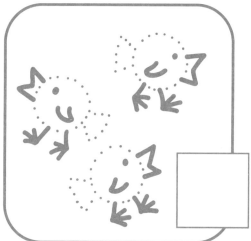 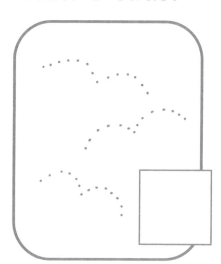

Join the sets of 3 to the number.

3

Matching Numbers

About 4. Count how many.
Write the number.

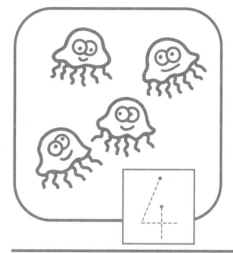

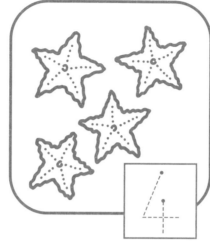

Draw 4 shells.

Draw 4 fish.

Draw 4 spades.

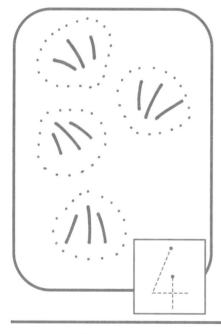

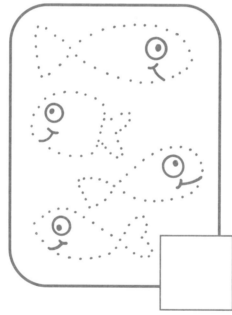

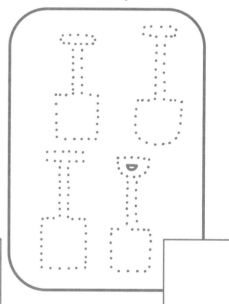

Join the sets of 4 to the number.

4

Matching Numbers

About 5. Count how many.
Write the number.

Draw 5 leaves.   Draw 5 acorns.   Draw 5 sticks.

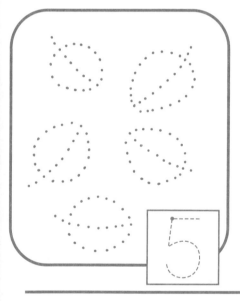

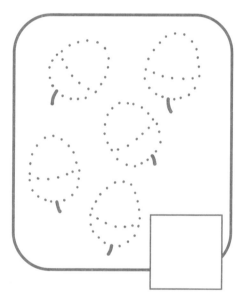

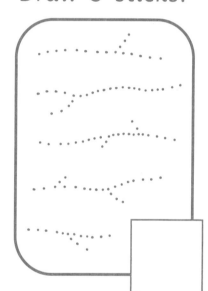

Join the sets of 5 to the number.

5

Schofield & Sims

the long-established educational publisher
specialising in maths, English and science materials for schools

Nursery Numbers is a series of graded activity books that reinforce mathematical language and early number skills, including matching, sequencing and counting. The books cover concepts such as money, shapes and measures and feature the appealing character of **Scamp the dog**.

Nursery Numbers Book 1 includes:

- Numbers to 5
- Simple shapes
- One-to-one matching
- Comparisons (for example, longer/shorter and more/less).

The full range of titles in the series is as follows:

Nursery Numbers Book 1:   ISBN 978 07217 0867 6

Nursery Numbers Book 2:   ISBN 978 07217 0868 3

Nursery Numbers Book 3:   ISBN 978 07217 0869 0

Nursery Numbers Book 4:   ISBN 978 07217 0870 6

Nursery Numbers Book 5:   ISBN 978 07217 0906 2

Nursery Numbers Book 6:   ISBN 978 07217 0907 9

Have you tried **Nursery Writing** by Schofield & Sims?
This series uses **Eddy the teddy** to help young children learn letters,
sounds and simple words.

**For further information and to place your order
visit www.schofieldandsims.co.uk or telephone 01484 607080**

First edition copyright © Schofield and Sims Ltd, 2001
Fifteenth impression 2012
Author: Sally Johnson

Printed in the UK by Wyndeham Gait Ltd, Grimsby, Lincolnshire

ISBN 978-07217-0867-6

9 780721 708676

Schofield & Sims

Dogley Mill, Fenay Bridge, Huddersfield HD8 0NQ
Phone: 01484 607080 Facsimile: 01484 606815
E-mail: sales@schofieldandsims.co.uk

ISBN 978 07217 0867 6

**£2.45
(Retail price)**

Early Years Foundation Stage
Age range: 3–5 years